Sheltie and the Snow Pony

Make friends with

Sheltie

The little pony with the big heart

Sheltie is the lovable little Shetland pony with a big personality. His best friend and owner is Emma, and together they have lots of exciting adventures.

Share Sheltie and Emma's adventures in

SHELTIE THE SHETLAND PONY
SHELTIE SAVES THE DAY
SHELTIE AND THE RUNAWAY
SHELTIE FINDS A FRIEND
SHELTIE TO THE RESCUE
SHELTIE IN DANGER
SHELTIE RIDES TO WIN
SHELTIE AND THE SADDLE MYSTERY
SHELTIE LEADS THE WAY
SHELTIE THE HERO
SHELTIE IN TROUBLE
SHELTIE AND THE STRAY

Peter Clover was born and went to school in London. He was a storyboard artist and illustrator before he began to put words to his pictures. He enjoys painting, travelling, cooking and keeping fit, and lives on the coast in Somerset.

Also by Peter Clover in Puffin

The Sheltie series

Sheltie and the Snow Pony

Peter Clover

PUFFIN BOOKS

For Yvette, Bob and Bruno

PUFFIN BOOKS

Published by the Penguin Group
Penguin Books Ltd, 27 Wrights Lane, London W8 5TZ, England
Penguin Putnam Inc., 375 Hudson Street, New York, New York 10014, USA
Penguin Books Australia Ltd, Ringwood, Victoria, Australia
Penguin Books Canada Ltd, 10 Alcorn Avenue, Toronto, Ontario, Canada M4V 3B2
Penguin Books (NZ) Ltd, Private Bag 102902, NSMC, Auckland, New Zealand

On the World Wide Web at: www.penguin.com

Penguin Books Ltd, Registered Offices: Harmondsworth, Middlesex, England

First published 1999
5 7 9 10 8 6 4

Created by Working Partners Ltd, London, W6 OQT

The moral right of the author has been asserted

Set in 14/22 Palatino

Made and printed in England by Clays Ltd, St Ives plc

British Library Cataloguing in Publication Data
A CIP catalogue record for this book is available from the British Library

ISBN 0–141–30448–0

Chapter One

'Brrr!' Emma shivered in her thick jacket. The wind outside was cold enough to freeze her breath.

She stood on the cottage step and hugged herself to keep warm. Looking up to the sky, she blew white, frosty puffs into the air.

On the ground everything, as far as Emma could see, was covered in a dusting of white.

'Jack Frost was busy last night,' she said. She pulled up her collar and crunched her way across the grass to the paddock.

Two small ears pricked up expectantly from a wild, unruly mop of frosted forelock. And a pair of gentle brown eyes twinkled brightly as Emma approached. Sheltie, her little Shetland pony, stood waiting with his fuzzy chin resting on the top bar of the wooden gate.

Sheltie could see the apple that Emma was holding. He blew a cheeky snort and she scratched him hard between his ears.

'Good morning, boy. Look what I've got for you!'

The apple was soon gone as Sheltie

munched happily, pushing his soft
nose into Emma's gloved hand
looking for more.

Emma swung her legs over the fence
and walked with Sheltie to his field
shelter. Sheltie walked close and kept
nudging Emma playfully with his
muzzle. Emma nudged Sheltie back.
But as she leaned into him, Sheltie
suddenly skipped sideways and Emma
sat down with a bump.

'Ow!' laughed Emma. 'You're
obviously full of tricks this morning,
Sheltie.' Then, as Emma sat on the
frosty grass she felt something cold
touch her face. It was a snowflake
landing gently on her cheek.

'Oh, Sheltie!' said Emma. 'It's
snowing.'

Sheltie looked up to the sky at the
fine, white snowflakes floating down
from the clouds. Emma broke the ice
on Sheltie's water trough and fished
out the frozen bits with her trowel.

'Come on, Sheltie. Breakfast!' Emma scooped the pony mix into the feed manger and watched as Sheltie wolfed down the lot.

Sheltie liked his food. If Emma wasn't careful, she would have a pony that was as fat as a barrel!

'Your trouble is that you're spoilt rotten,' said Emma. 'You've got everything you could possibly wish for, haven't you?'

Sheltie gave Emma a cheeky look, then nuzzled up closely and shut his eyes contentedly.

Emma gave Sheltie a kiss. His thick winter coat smelt of fresh air and snow. And he looked just like a big, cuddly toy.

After filling Sheltie's hay net, Emma

went back indoors for her own breakfast. The kitchen was warm and cosy, with pine cupboards and bright-red gingham curtains. Bacon sizzled under the grill and the smell made Emma's mouth water as she stepped inside, out of the cold.

After breakfast, Mum asked, 'What are you going to do today, Emma? Dad's taking me and Joshua shopping in Rilchester. Do you want to come?'

Emma liked going out with Mum and Dad. But she would rather take Sheltie out for a ride in the snowy countryside any day.

'I thought I might take Sheltie out over the downs,' said Emma. 'To see if it's been snowing up there.'

'Poor old Sheltie,' laughed Mum. 'I

6

bet he'd much rather stay in his nice, comfortable paddock!'

'No, he wouldn't,' said Emma. 'Anyway, I'm keeping him fit. Exercise is good for ponies.'

Mum didn't dare argue.

'I expect you're right,' she said. 'When it comes to Sheltie, Emma, you always know best.'

Mum, Dad and Joshua left for Rilchester soon after breakfast. Emma put on an extra jumper under her jacket and wrapped her favourite scarf round her neck. Then she adjusted her riding hat, fixed the strap under her chin and went out to tack up Sheltie.

The paddock gleamed white beneath its light covering of snow.

Sheltie pranced and snorted, pawing

a hole in the snow with his hoof. The little pony was eager to be off and away. He loved going out, whatever the weather.

Emma walked Sheltie out into the lane. Then they crossed the snow-covered meadow at a trot as they headed for Bramble Wood and the downs beyond.

The freezing wind made Emma's eyes run and her face turn pink. But Sheltie didn't seem to feel the cold at all. His thick, hairy coat and shaggy mane kept him nice and warm.

Emma crouched low over Sheltie's neck as she rode him faster across the downs. It hadn't been snowing much up there after all. Sheltie's hoofs drummed the hard ground.

'We're going to win, Sheltie! We're going to win!' Emma was pretending that they were in a race. She was so lost in her game that she didn't take much notice of where she was heading.

Sheltie finally slowed down to a walk.

'Where are we, Sheltie?' Emma looked around.

She suddenly realized that they were on the East Down. Emma urged Sheltie to follow a path that wound its way through a valley. The valley would lead them back to Barrow Hill and the village of Little Applewood, where Emma lived.

Before long they were riding in the valley and following a bridle path which suddenly forked off in two directions.

Emma knew that one path led to the village. She wasn't sure where the other path led.

'Come on, Sheltie! Let's go exploring.'

Sheltie sniffed at the air. Then he

shook out his mane and jangled his
reins, eager to follow the new path.

Chapter Two

Emma and Sheltie found themselves in a very narrow, overgrown lane, deep set between tall hedges and trees that almost met overhead. The hedges and trees were icy and frosted white.

'Oh, look, Sheltie,' said Emma. 'A snow tunnel.'

Halfway down the tunnel Sheltie's ears pricked up. Emma heard something too! It was the sound of a pony neighing. And it was coming from somewhere behind the hedge.

Sheltie found a gap and Emma peered through into someone's garden. It wasn't much of a garden really. More of a dry frozen patch with bushes and bare trees. And there right in the middle, tethered to one of those trees, was a small, brown pony.

The rope that tethered the pony had wound itself round the poor creature's legs. It stood there unable to move.

Emma quickly found a gate hidden in the hedge. Without a second thought, she slid off Sheltie and walked with him up to the back door of the cottage.

The brown pony looked up with big, sad eyes. Sheltie called to the pony with a soft whicker. He seemed to know that this pony was in trouble.

Emma noticed a nameplate which said 'Lewis' next to the door knocker. She knocked loudly on the door and waited.

It took ages before the door opened. But when it did, a smartly dressed

woman stood on the step, whom
Emma assumed was Mrs Lewis.

'Hello,' the woman said with a
bright, friendly smile. 'Are you selling
something?'

Emma was taken aback. 'No, I'm
not,' she said. 'It's your pony!'

'My pony?' The woman seemed
puzzled.

'Yes, your pony!' said Emma. 'He's very tangled up in his rope. His tether is far too long and it's all wound round his legs.'

'Oh no, not again,' replied the woman. 'The silly thing keeps doing that! You couldn't give me a hand, could you? Only I'm hopeless with animals.'

Pulling the door closed on the latch behind her, the woman beckoned Emma and Sheltie to follow her down the garden. She held Sheltie's rein while Emma approached the pony. As she untied the cord from the tree, Emma felt a wave of pity pass over her for the poor tethered animal.

The pony watched Emma's every

move as she carefully untangled the rope.

As soon as he was free, the pony ambled over to Sheltie and rubbed noses.

'Oh!' squealed the woman. 'What are they doing? They're not going to fight, are they?' She held Sheltie's rein at arm's length.

Emma couldn't help giggling. 'They're just saying hello!' she said. 'That's how ponies do it. They rub noses.'

'Oh, I can see you're an expert,' the woman said, smiling. And she really meant it.

'Well, I do know quite a bit about ponies,' said Emma. She wanted to tell the woman that this pony looked too thin. That the poor thing would freeze without a rug or a shelter. And that there wasn't nearly enough grass for the pony to graze. It needed pony feed and sweet, fresh hay. And water.

But Emma didn't say any of these things. She didn't want to sound rude. So instead she asked, 'How old is he?'

'Oh my!' said the woman. 'I've no idea.'

'Is he *your* pony?' inquired Emma.

'Well, yes, he is now,' she said. 'I saw Prince advertised in the newspaper as an abandoned stray and bought him for my daughter. She's away at boarding school at the moment. We live up-country, but we often come here for weekends and stay at the cottage.

'The dealer said that he had been abandoned on the moor. He's a rescue pony, you see, and I thought Jessica would love to have him. We thought it would make a nice surprise present for her birthday next week.'

Emma listened to this with interest.

'Mind you,' the woman continued,

'since he was delivered two days ago
he's been nothing but trouble. But then
I don't know much about ponies.'

Emma looked at Prince. She
couldn't imagine him being any
trouble at all. The brown pony nuzzled

up to Sheltie as though he had found a long-lost friend. Sheltie looked so fat standing next to him. Sheltie's thick woolly coat would keep him warm in the coldest weather. And his plump belly would never be empty.

Emma wanted to do something to help poor Prince. She wanted Prince to feel loved and wanted too.

'I hope he's going to be an excellent jumper,' said the woman suddenly.

'Does Jessica like jumping?' asked Emma.

'Well, I expect she will once she's learned to ride,' said the woman.

A look of surprise swept across Emma's face. Jessica had never even ridden a pony! Suddenly, Emma couldn't keep quiet any longer.

'But what about a stable for Prince when you're not here?' said Emma. 'The poor thing will freeze in this weather. He looks so cold already!'

'Oh, don't worry about that, my dear girl,' said the woman. 'He's going to some stables for winter boarding. He's too much of a handful for me to keep here on my own.'

Emma breathed a sigh of relief. At least the pony was going to have a roof over his head and some warm straw for the winter. Perhaps this woman wasn't so scatterbrained after all.

'Which stables are going to board him?' asked Emma. 'Will it be Crossways?'

'Oh, I haven't decided yet,' the

woman said vaguely. 'I've got to make some inquiries.' She looked at her watch. 'Well, I must go now. Thank you for your help.'

'If you like, I'll shorten his tether for you so he won't get tangled up again,' said Emma. 'And if you've got an old blanket, I'll show you how to make a rug to keep him warm.'

'That's very kind of you,' said the woman. 'But I don't think we have any old blankets. We only use duvets. You can shorten his rope if you like while I have a look!' Then she checked her watch again and hurried back inside leaving Emma and Sheltie alone with the poor, shivering pony.

Chapter Three

Emma shortened Prince's tether as she said she would, then rubbed at the hard, icy ground with the toe of her boot. She scraped away the frost and said, 'Look at that, Sheltie! He's already cropped back the grass to the bare earth. There's nothing here at all for poor Prince to graze.' Then she noticed a laurel tree growing in the garden. 'And that laurel's poisonous to ponies,' she added. 'I'll adjust his tether again, Sheltie, just to make sure Prince can't reach those leaves.'

Then she went to say goodbye to the thin, gentle pony.

Mrs Lewis came back to say that she didn't have any old blankets, then she rushed off again.

Emma had a plan.

'Don't worry, boy,' she said to Prince. 'We'll come back this afternoon with a nice warm rug and some proper feed.'

Prince pushed his soft muzzle into Emma's chest and whickered quietly.

Emma noticed that the old headcollar he wore had been marked with his name. 'Prince' it said, in faded letters.

'Someone must have loved you once,' said Emma. She thought hard about what the dealer had said to Mrs Lewis about Prince being abandoned. 'What kind of person could possibly have abandoned you?' Then Emma gave the pony a big hug.

*

That afternoon, after lunch, Emma and Sheltie came back with an old blanket, some lengths of soft rope, and a carrier bag stuffed with hay and pony feed.

As they rode through the white tunnel, small snowflakes began to fall again. Sheltie let out a tremendous whinny as if he wanted to tell Prince they were coming.

The thin pony answered with a weak snort, and as they came into the garden the poor thing pricked up his ears and tried to greet them with a loud neigh. But he didn't seem to have the strength and just made a sad noise as he blew weakly through his lips.

Emma knocked at the back door and waited, but there was no answer.

'Maybe Mrs Lewis has gone to a

stable to organize Prince's boarding, Sheltie,' said Emma.

Sheltie shook out the snowflakes from his mane and blew a raspberry.

'Was that for her?' grinned Emma.

Sheltie pawed at the hard ground.

'I guess it was,' she said.

Emma got busy with the blanket and lengths of rope. Prince stood perfectly still while Emma threw the cover across the pony's bare back. She carefully tied two corners of the blanket across Prince's chest, then used the ropes like girths, to secure the makeshift rug in place.

'There!' said Emma when she had finished. 'Is that better, Prince?'

The pony seemed grateful and gave a friendly blow.

Next, Emma piled the hay beneath a
tree and tipped out the pony mix next
to it. Immediately, Prince wolfed down
the feed then began munching
hungrily on the hay.

Emma and Sheltie stayed with
Prince for half an hour. Then the snow
began to fall heavier than ever.

'We'd better go now,' said Emma.

She decided to look up 'Lewis' in the phone book when she got back to the cottage, to see if Prince *had* been booked into a stable.

'People shouldn't have ponies if they can't look after them,' said Emma. She hoped that Jessica Lewis would take better care of Prince than her mother did.

The snow continued to fall and by the time Emma arrived back at the cottage, thick drifts were already piling up against the hedges. She settled Sheltie into his shelter and went inside to look for Mrs Lewis's phone number.

There was only one Lewis listed in Little Applewood, and after tea, Emma rang the number several times. But there was no answer.

Mum could see that Emma was worried. Emma had told Mum all about Prince.

'Perhaps Mrs Lewis is visiting friends, Emma,' suggested Mum. 'Or maybe she's at the stables, getting Prince settled in!'

'I wonder which stables are boarding Prince,' said Emma. 'Crossways are the nearest.'

'Would you like me to give them a ring, Emma?' said Mum. 'Just to put your mind at rest.'

'Yes, please. Only it's snowing really hard now. And if Prince isn't stabled anywhere, he could freeze to death!'

Mum made several telephone calls.

She spoke to Crossways, Castles and two other stables in the area. But none were winter-boarding a dark brown pony called Prince. And none of them had even spoken to a Mrs Lewis about such a possibility.

'There *are* more stables, towards Rilchester,' said Mum.

'But they're miles away,' said Emma. 'Why would Mrs Lewis board Prince at a stable that it takes ages to get to? If Jessica Lewis is going to ride Prince, then she'd want him to be near!'

Mum knew that Emma was right.

'Maybe winter-boarding at a stable was too expensive,' suggested Mum. 'Perhaps Mrs Lewis has tried to find a farmer with an empty barn.'

Emma listened. But she had already decided what she was going to do. Whatever arrangements Mrs Lewis had made, Emma was going to ride over, first thing in the morning, and find out for herself.

Chapter Four

Later that evening, Emma asked Mum if she could telephone Sally. Sally was Emma's best friend and had a pony called Minnow. Sally had been away with her mother for a few days, visiting an aunt, but she had returned to Little Applewood that evening.

Emma wanted to tell Sally all about Prince. She knew without asking that Sally would want to help.

'. . . so I'll meet you in the morning,'
said Emma.

'I'll be there,' said Sally. 'Nine
o'clock.'

*

Next morning, after a quick breakfast, Emma tacked up Sheltie and stuffed two carrier bags full with hay. Then she scooped some pony mix into a third bag.

Sheltie watched all this with great interest. His own haynet was bulging and he had already gobbled up his breakfast. Sheltie cocked his head to one side.

'I bet you're wondering who this is for, aren't you, Sheltie?' said Emma. 'Well, it's for Prince. If he's still at the Lewises' cottage, then he'll be glad of a good feed.'

Sheltie blew frosty puffs from his nostrils. The morning was cold and crisp. And there were at least five centimetres of snow on the ground.

Sheltie enjoyed the snow. He liked trampling through the deeper white drifts and lifting his hoofs high. His long tail brushed the snowy lane and at times his fat belly dipped into soft, snowy mounds.

Emma rode carefully, keeping Sheltie in the centre of the lanes. She didn't want him stumbling into any hidden dips or holes.

Emma and Sheltie looked up at all the rooftops. They were completely covered with snow. It looked like a topping of whipped cream.

'Isn't it lovely, Sheltie?' said Emma. She leaned forward and clapped the little pony's neck. And as she did so, a snowball flew past her head.

'Who threw that?' Emma sat upright

in the saddle. She couldn't see anyone.
A second snowball hit Sheltie smack
on the forelock, right on top of his
head.

Sheltie harrumphed playfully, then
blew a raspberry and looked across

towards a large, white, snow-covered bush.

Emma followed Sheltie's lead and steered him nearer for a better look.

'It's Sally,' whispered Emma. 'Look, Sheltie. There's Minnow's rump sticking out.'

Sheltie could see his pony friend's tail swishing backwards and forwards. Sheltie's ears pricked up instantly.

Emma slid out of the saddle and quickly made an enormous snowball. Then she pointed to the other side of the bush and hoped Sheltie would trot round on his own.

Sheltie seemed to understand and did what Emma thought he would. Emma crept around the other way.

Sally was quite surprised to see

Sheltie on his own. But she was even more surprised when a snowball the size of a grapefruit exploded on top of her riding hat.

'Gotcha!' yelled Emma, as she leaped into view from behind.

Sally burst out laughing. Minnow threw back his head and blew a loud snicker. After all, he hadn't expected to

be showered with snow. Sheltie added
to the fun by butting Emma with his
nose, sending her flying headlong into
the snow-covered bush.

'That'll teach you to sneak up on
people!' smiled Sally, brushing snow
from her shoulders.

Emma grinned. It was great having
a friend like Sally.

Sheltie and Minnow walked along side
by side. They trundled through the
snow, kicking up their heels as more
flurries slowly drifted down from the
sky. Sheltie gave a snort as they
approached the snow tunnel which led
to the Lewises' cottage.

Before they reached the gate in the
long hedge, Sheltie seemed worried.

41

He stopped, flicked up his ears and sniffed at the icy breeze.

'What is it, boy?' said Emma. 'What's the matter?'

Emma's little Shetland pony called out with a whinny. It was almost as if he were trying to tell Emma that something was very wrong.

Sheltie and Minnow stopped at the wooden gate and stood to attention, side by side. Sheltie poked his head over the top bar and blew an urgent snort.

Emma and Sally gasped aloud, then looked on in horror. There was a brown heap lying on the snow-covered ground. It was Prince!

Emma quickly slipped down from the saddle and ran straight into the

garden with Sheltie trotting after her.
Sally tethered Minnow loosely to a
shrub and rushed to help.

'Knock on the door,' said Emma.
'See if Mrs Lewis is in.'

Sally knocked and knocked, but
there was no reply.

The snow was falling heavier now

and Emma was already on her knees brushing snowflakes off Prince's head. Sheltie softly nuzzled the brown pony's forelock.

Prince's eyes flickered, and he paddled feebly with his forelegs. Emma felt tears pricking her eyes. The poor pony didn't have the strength to get himself up.

'Oh, Emma!' croaked Sally. 'He looks terrible. What shall we do?'

'We've got to get him warm,' said Emma. 'And quickly.' She tipped out one of the hay-filled carrier bags and grabbed two big fistfuls.

'Come on, Sally. We'll rub him warm.' She felt Prince's legs. They were ice cold. 'Legs first!'

The two girls used the pads of hay

to rub the pony's legs. Emma worked her way up to his shoulder, rubbing hard, trying to make the pony warm. Sally rubbed too and worked her way along his back to his rump.

Prince stirred and tried to lift his head. But he was far too weak. The snow continued to fall, but luckily the blanket that Emma had tied was still in place. It had slipped a little though, so Emma pulled at it to cover Prince's bare shoulder. Then she stuffed some hay underneath.

'I think it's working,' said Emma. 'Keep rubbing, Sally!'

'But we can't stay here all morning,' said Sally. 'Shouldn't one of us go for help before this snow gets worse?'

While Emma was thinking what to

do, Sheltie laid himself down next to Prince and gently pressed his warm back against the thin pony's back.

'Oh, look,' said Sally. 'Sheltie's trying to help.'

'You keep rubbing, Sally. I'll take Sheltie's saddle off so he can get closer.'

Prince opened his eyes and blew the softest, quietest whicker that Emma and Sally had ever heard.

'He's got hardly any strength at all,' said Sally.

'But I think he's getting warmer,' said Emma. 'I'll stay here with Sheltie. You take Minnow and go and knock on one of the cottages further up the lane. Tell them what's happened and ask them to call Mr Thorne the vet.

Tell them it's urgent!'

Sally jumped up and rushed back towards Minnow. She cleared his saddle with the sleeve of her jacket.

'Come on, boy. This is a real emergency.' Sally quickly mounted and took Minnow up the lane as fast as she dared.

Chapter Five

Emma tried to tempt Prince with a handful of pony mix, but he was too weak even to eat.

'Don't die, Prince. Please don't die,' whispered Emma. 'Try to hang on just a bit longer. Sally will bring help and everything will be all right, you'll see! Just hang on. Please!'

Emma wrapped her arms around the pony's neck and carried on rubbing until her shoulders ached. Sheltie's thick winter coat felt warm against Prince's back. Emma was glad Sheltie was there. He kept making soft noises which seemed to reassure the sick pony.

Emma snuggled down with the two ponies and tried to keep warm herself. The air had turned icy cold and the sky was a grubby white. It looked as if there was still a lot of snow to fall.

Snowflakes fell and settled on them as they lay there, waiting. Emma kept brushing them off. But no sooner had she cleared the snow than a fresh covering laid itself upon them.

Emma shivered. She was beginning to feel the cold herself.

Emma talked to Prince. He seemed to be listening and twitched his ears.

'Don't worry, Prince. Sally will be here soon with help.' But Emma was thinking, What's happened to her? Why is it taking so long? She stroked both ponies' faces and Sheltie whickered gently. He seemed to be saying. 'I'm still here. I'll keep you warm.'

Emma was wondering whether she should leave Prince for a while and take Sheltie to look for Sally and Minnow. She was beginning to think that something had happened to them, when she heard the sound of car tyres crunching snow outside in the lane on the other side of the hedge. Then she heard Sally's voice calling.

'Emma. Emma. We're here!'

Sally rushed into the garden. 'This is

Mr Baker from the last cottage up the lane. No one else along the way was in,' breathed Sally heavily. 'I had to go right to the end and it took ages. Mrs Baker has called the vet and Mr Baker has come to help. He knows all about ponies.'

Mr Baker had brought a duvet from his spare bedroom and some nice thick blankets. He wrapped one around Emma, then threw the duvet and two other blankets across Prince.

Sheltie rolled up on to his feet and shook the snow from his thick shaggy coat. Mr Baker began rubbing Prince all over just like Emma and Sally had, to help warm him up.

Sheltie tossed his head and shook more snow from his mane. Then he

looked towards the hedge as he heard
the sound of another vehicle pulling
up outside in the lane.

Emma rushed to see who it was. It
was Mr Thorne, the vet, driving a
horsebox.

The snow continued to fall as Mr Thorne came through the gate and joined them.

The vet bent over Prince with a stethoscope, shaking his head. Prince didn't move.

'Is he dead?' asked Emma nervously.

'No,' said Mr Thorne. 'But he's in a very bad way. It's a good job you came along when you did.' He rooted around in his bag and gave Prince an injection.

Just then, Mrs Baker came running into the garden. She had stayed behind to make sure the vet was coming, and now hurried to help them.

'Oh, the Lewises' poor pony. Mrs

Lewis told my neighbour that their daughter had had an accident at school and she had to drop everything and drive up-country first thing this morning. She was still desperate to find Prince a winter stable, but hadn't had time.'

'That's no excuse,' said Mr Thorne. 'What this pony needs now is warmth and tender loving care.'

Mrs Lewis had seemed to have forgotten all about getting Prince into a stable and had hurried off in a panic to be with her daughter.

'The dealer should never have let Mrs Lewis have Prince without first telling her how to care for him,' said Mr Thorne. 'Let's see if we can get him on to his feet, then once in the horsebox we can decide what to do with him.'

'He can come and stay with us,' said Emma. 'There's plenty of room in Sheltie's field shelter.'

Mr Thorne called Emma's dad on his mobile phone and made sure it would be OK.

They managed to get Prince on to his feet, but he was very weak and wobbly on his legs.

Sheltie nuzzled up to the pony and blew encouraging snorts. It was almost as though Sheltie was trying to get Prince to follow him.

Whatever Sheltie's snorts meant, Prince understood. And with everyone helping, the pony managed to walk slowly up the ramp and into the

waiting horsebox. Mr Baker said he
would drive while the vet stayed in
the back with Prince.

The snow was very thick out in the
lane, and the going was hard and
slow. Emma and Sally followed behind
the horsebox on Sheltie and Minnow.

When they reached Sally's turn off, Emma said goodbye and followed the horsebox alone. She walked Sheltie in the deep ruts that the tyres made in the snow.

Once outside Emma's cottage, Emma rode Sheltie right up through the garden to the kitchen and called out for Mum and Dad to come and help.

Chapter Six

While Mr Thorne tended to Prince in the horsebox and gave him another injection, Emma told her parents everything that had happened. She untacked Sheltie, then helped Dad lay a thick bedding of straw across the floor of the field shelter.

Mum came out with an extra-thick blanket as Prince was settled down on the soft bed and gave a long sigh.

Mum covered him with the warm rug and knelt down to stroke his tired face.

'There, there, Prince,' she said. 'We'll look after you and make you better. You poor pony.'

Dad hung up a heat lamp, and connected it to his spare car-battery. Then he watched as Sheltie lay down again next to Prince and snuggled up close to give the pony some extra warmth.

'You'll need to feed him bran mashes for a few days until he gets his strength back,' said the vet. 'Little and often. But it's nice and cosy in here out of the snow. What he needs more than anything is warmth and company. And I think Sheltie is going to see to that, aren't you, boy?'

Sheltie raised his head and blew a soft snort.

Emma knew Sheltie would do everything he could to help Prince. Even if it meant lying as close as possible to him through the night.

After the vet left to drive Mr Baker home, Dad went to chop some more logs for the fire and Mum went back to the cottage to check on Joshua, who was having a nap.

Emma sat with the two ponies for a while, to make sure Prince was settled. She stroked the pony's neck and smiled. 'He already feels a lot warmer, Sheltie,' she said.

Prince opened his eyes and looked around him. He seemed happy to be somewhere safe and warm.

Later, Emma helped Mum to prepare a bran mash for Prince, and hand-fed him as he lay on his bed of straw. The starved pony took the feed hungrily.

'Don't give him too much, Emma. Little and often was what the vet said,' smiled Mum.

Emma glanced up. 'He is going to be all right, isn't he?' she asked.

'I think he will be,' said Mum. 'Mr Thorne said he would look in tomorrow to check Prince's progress. And the injections seem to be helping.'

It was true. Prince already seemed a happier pony. And his coat felt warm under Emma's hand.

The next morning, Emma woke bright and early. The snow had stopped falling and the sky was now clear and blue. Birds sang in the bare branches of the trees. And as Emma rubbed the window pane and cleared a peephole in the frosty glass, she saw a wonderful sight out in the paddock.

Everything as far as she could see

was covered in a crisp white blanket of snow. And there, waiting by the paddock gate, were Sheltie and Prince. The pony had pulled himself to his feet to take a look at the outside world, and had followed Sheltie over to the fence. He still looked wobbly on his legs. But he was standing on his own and looked interested in everything around him.

Emma hurried downstairs to make a breakfast mash for Prince before school. She nursed the bowl carefully and carried it out to the paddock.

'Breakfast time,' called Emma.

Sheltie seemed to know that the bowl of mash wasn't for him and waited patiently for his own breakfast while Emma fed Prince first.

'That's a good boy, Sheltie,' said Emma. 'You know Prince is hungry, don't you?'

Sheltie nuzzled Prince with his soft muzzle and watched him feed. And he didn't try to steal one mouthful. Sheltie waited until Prince had finished and then Sheltie stuck his nose in and licked the bowl clean.

'It's your turn now, Sheltie,' laughed Emma as she scooped pony mix into the feed manger.

Sheltie wolfed down most of it, then stepped back to offer Prince some of his own breakfast.

The brown pony looked at the mix in the manger, then whickered softly and took the last few pieces.

'You can have some more of that

later, Prince,' said Emma. 'But we
don't want to give you too much just
yet.'

Prince pushed his nose into Emma's
hand and licked her palm. He was
such a sweet pony.

Over the next few days, Prince made a
remarkable recovery.

'He's a tough chap,' said Mr Thorne
when he came on his visits. 'And
really quite a healthy pony. At first I
was worried that he might have
caught pneumonia. But it was just the
cold that had got to him. He's going to
be fine!'

Sheltie nudged the vet with his head
and blew a cheeky raspberry.

'Prince doesn't have a nice thick

winter coat like you, Sheltie,' he
added. 'So keeping him out of the
weather was the best cure – that and
proper feeding. This sort of thing
happens sometimes when people take
on animals without thinking it
through first.'

The paddock was still covered with
snow so there was no grass to graze.

But there was plenty of hay and as much pony mix as Prince needed. Emma fed him chopped carrots and apples too. She liked having two ponies to look after.

Every day Prince grew stronger. His ears weren't so floppy and his eyes became bright and lively. He even enjoyed a romp or two with Sheltie, chasing round the paddock in games of 'Catch me if you can' and 'Tag'.

It was still freezing cold outside. But Mum had borrowed a proper pony rug, and Prince felt nice and warm. And at night he and Sheltie slept in the field shelter.

On Saturday when the vet called, he had some news from Mrs Lewis. Mrs Baker had managed to contact her and had told her all about Prince and what had happened.

'Mrs Lewis will be staying with her daughter in their other house,' said Mr Thorne.

'Is Jessica all right?' asked Emma.

'Jessica's fine, but apparently they won't be coming back down for weeks. Mrs Lewis is very worried about Prince, though, and now thinks that having a weekend pony doesn't seem like such a good idea after all. She doesn't think she will be able to look after Prince properly.'

'So it looks as though we have an unwanted orphan on our hands,' said Mum.

Mr Thorne raised his eyebrows. 'Mrs Lewis asked if you wouldn't mind looking after him and try to find Prince a nice home with someone who could care for him properly. She feels terrible that Prince got so ill. Her intentions were good but she just didn't think.'

Mum and Dad discussed the problem.

'Well, Mrs Lewis has offered to pay all expenses and vet's bills so I suppose Prince will be no trouble,' said Mum.

'And there's plenty of room in Sheltie's paddock,' added Emma brightly.

Sheltie blew a loud snort. He seemed to like the idea too! Having a live-in friend was great fun for the little Shetland pony.

'Perhaps the riding school will take him on,' suggested Dad. 'He's a bright pony and very friendly.'

'That *would* be best for Prince,' said Mum. 'After all, he's going to need exercising. And you have your hands more than full with Sheltie, Emma.'

Emma knew that Mum was right.

'But we won't do anything just yet,' said Dad. 'We'll get him as fit as a fiddle first. Then we'll decide.'

Emma felt happier about that! At least she could look after Prince until then. And if he *did* go to the riding school, she knew he would be looked after properly.

Chapter Seven

Two weeks passed and the snow
disappeared as quickly as it had come.
The paddock was green again with
plenty of grass for the two ponies to
graze.

Prince rounded out nicely and
looked like a completely different
pony. He followed Sheltie everywhere
and wouldn't leave his little friend's
side.

When Emma went out riding she took Prince along on a lead rein. And he was happy to trot alongside and go wherever Sheltie went.

One Saturday, Emma and Sheltie were riding with Sally and Minnow. They took Prince with them, and as it was such a beautiful sunny morning,

they decided to go for a long hack across the moor.

Emma liked riding on the moor. She loved the way it stretched out as far as they could see. And there were still parts which she and Sally hadn't explored fully.

As they rode side by side, chatting happily, they both noticed a slight change in Prince. The pony was still happy to walk on the lead rein, but he seemed to become more frisky and lightened his step the further they went on to the moor. He took deep breaths of cool, fresh moorland air and blew out long plumes of steam from his nostrils. Then his ears pricked up to attention and he tossed his head looking around at his surroundings.

'Prince seems to be really enjoying himself,' said Sally.

'I've never seem him look so happy,' smiled Emma.

Sheltie noticed too and blew funny pony snorts as though he were talking to his friend.

When they came to a part of the moor were neither Emma nor Sally had been before, Prince started pulling forward and decided to take the lead.

'Do you get the feeling that Prince knows where he is?' asked Sally.

'It's almost as though he recognizes this place,' agreed Emma. Then before either of them could say any more, Prince broke into a gentle trot.

Sheltie and Minnow quickened their pace and trotted too.

'I think Prince knows exactly where he is,' said Emma. 'Come on, Sally. Let's see where he wants to go. I'm sure he wants to take us somewhere!'

Emma let the lead rein out to its full length and Prince rolled into a slow canter.

Sheltie's little legs managed to keep up and Minnow's stride kept Sally alongside.

Six pairs of hoofs drummed the hard ground as the posse of three ponies and two riders covered the new stretch of moor.

They rode on for a few minutes. Then, without any warning, Prince turned to his right and began following a rough cart track. The track led towards a distant cottage half

hidden by a copse of trees.

Prince rushed up to the cottage wall and stood with his head over a gate looking into a little garden.

'Who could possibly live here?' said Sally.

'I've no idea,' answered Emma.

'But I think Prince knows.'

Prince threw up his head and whinnied loudly. Emma had never heard him make such a loud noise before. Then Sheltie joined in and finally Minnow as well. Between them the three ponies were making a terrible din.

Emma and Sally started to giggle. They both thought it was really funny, and hoped that whoever lived there didn't mind.

Suddenly the cottage door swung open and a grey-haired woman stepped out. Emma and Sally stopped laughing at once. The old lady's face looked very stern. Then she saw Prince and her face lit up with a huge smile.

'Prince! Is that you? My darling boy!' her voice sounded shaky and tired.

Prince blew another series of soft snorts.

'It *is* you! Oh, my darling boy, wherever have you been? Oh, what clever girls to find my darling Prince!'

Emma and Sally exchanged glances. This old lady was obviously Prince's original owner. Prince knew her immediately and pushed his velvety muzzle into her outstretched hand. Then the woman gave Prince's neck a big hug and her eyes turned watery with tears.

It was such a lovely scene. But all Emma could think about was how did Prince end up in Mrs Lewis's garden?

Surely this kind old lady wouldn't have abandoned Prince. She obviously loved him to pieces.

Emma could tell by Sally's face that she was thinking the same thing too.

The old lady opened the gate and let them all into the small garden. She said her name was Mrs Warner.

Prince immediately nuzzled up as close as he could to his long-lost owner.

'Come inside. I'll make some nice hot cocoa. Then we can sit by the fire and you can tell me where you found my darling Prince.'

Emma and Sally left Sheltie, Prince and Minnow to graze in the walled

garden. There were no flowers or vegetables for the ponies to destroy, and Mrs Warner seemed quite happy for them to be there.

Sheltie was extra curious and tried to follow Emma into the cottage.

'No!' said Emma. 'You wait outside with Prince and Minnow.'

'I don't mind,' said Mrs Warner. 'There's nothing in here that he can harm.'

Emma grinned. She liked this funny old lady. But she still wasn't going to allow Sheltie to come inside. 'He's got to learn that he can't just wander into people's houses whenever he feels like it,' Emma said.

Sheltie was quite happy to stand just outside the open door while Mrs

Warner told Prince's story. He stood very quietly in case he was shooed away.

'I'll make the cocoa first,' said Mrs Warner. Then she sat by the fire and began to tell them what had happened.

Chapter Eight

Emma and Sally listened carefully to everything that Mrs Warner said.

'When my husband died last year, I didn't think I would be able to keep Prince. But Harry loved that pony. And so do I,' she added, 'with all my heart. So I kept Prince on and tried to manage as best I could. He had originally belonged to our grandson, but when the family had moved to

Australia, we'd agreed to take care of him.

'After Harry's death, the price of hay got too high and I started letting Prince out on to the moor to graze. He seemed quite safe, and always came back. Every night, like clockwork, he'd come trotting through the garden gate and round to his little stable at the back.' Mrs Warner's voice trailed off and she looked down at her slippers.

Emma sipped her cocoa. 'What happened then?' she asked.

Mrs Warner looked up again. 'Well, one day he didn't come back. Prince just disappeared and I haven't seen him from then to this day. I tried to find Prince. I walked the moor, and pinned up notices, but I heard nothing.'

Emma guessed what must have happened.

'Prince must have wandered further out on to the moor than he intended,' said Emma, 'and been mistaken for a stray. The dealer must have taken Prince and sold him to Mrs Lewis. She probably thought she was doing Prince a good turn.'

Emma told Mrs Warner all about Mrs Lewis. The old lady looked very upset when she heard what had happened.

'I expect there was a notice in the newspaper, but I never read the papers these days. Oh, my poor darling Prince,' she said. 'I would never have

abandoned him or turned him out
on to the moor to fend for himself.
There's been a terrible mistake.'

Then Emma told Mrs Warner of
Dad's idea about the riding stables.

Mrs Warner brightened a little
when she heard about that.

'Well, I can't really afford to keep
him any more,' she said. 'So I expect
that if the stables *did* take him on,
he would at least be well cared
for.'

'And you could go and see him
whenever you wanted,' added Sally.

It seemed like a very good idea and
the perfect solution.

Mrs Warner thought about it for a
moment, then said. 'If this riding
stables is near the moor and promises

to take care of him, then I suppose it will be the best thing for Prince after all. He used to love being ridden. And he loves children too.'

'Why don't I ask my dad to inquire at the stables for you?' suggested Emma. 'You can keep him here until we have any news if you like!'

'Maybe it's best in the long run if you take him with you and arrange it all,' said Mrs Warner. 'He seems happy enough to be with you and you've done an excellent job of taking care of him so far.'

Sheltie seemed to agree and gave a loud snort that made Mrs Warner jump. They had forgotten all about Sheltie for a moment. He had been so quiet, standing there on the doorstep.

They said their goodbyes, then
Emma and Sally took Prince home.

Dad contacted the riding stables
straight away and they said they
would be very happy to take Prince.
They wanted to see him first, but
when they heard the whole story they
were almost certain that they could
give Prince a good home for life.
Someone would come round later that
day to have a look at him.

The next day, Sunday, Emma and
Sheltie delivered Prince to the stables.
It wasn't Crossways. It was Castles,
the one nearer the moor. But first, they
took him to say goodbye to Mrs
Warner.

Prince seemed to know that he was

going to a new home and nuzzled up
to the old lady to say farewell. His
coat shone in the winter sunshine and
his eyes twinkled brightly like
diamonds.

Mrs Warner's eyes filled with tears
as she gave Prince one last hug.

'We have friends who ride at the
stables,' said Emma. 'And we'll make
sure that we come riding this way as
often as we can.'

'Thank you, my dear,' said Mrs
Warner. 'At least I can stop worrying
about Prince now. It's such a relief
to know where he is. And I'll write
to Mrs Lewis and tell her what's
happened. I'm sure she meant well.
But it's a good job that you and Sheltie
came along when you did!'

'Sheltie has a nose for trouble,' laughed Emma.

'Well, it's a good job he has,' smiled Mrs Warner.

Sheltie threw up his head and blew a raspberry. Then he pranced on the spot, eager to get going and deliver his friend to his new home at Castles' riding school. Stables fit for a Prince.